Trish Poodle's
BAD HAIR DAY

written by Jennifer Coleman
illustrated by Tiffany Young

McGraw-Hill
School Division

New York   Farmington

"There are only four days until my party, and there is so much to do," said Trish Poodle to her friend, Deena. "I need to buy a cake, some apples, juice and milk. I need to get plates and cups, and many balloons."

"Sounds like fun," said Deena. "I will help you."

"Oh, I need a hair cut, too," said Trish. "I will do that first. Can you meet me here at three o'clock? Then we can go shopping."

"Okay," said Deena, "tomorrow at three."

At three the next day, Deena knocked on Trish's door.

"Go away," said Trish.

"It's me. It's Deena."

"Go away," said Trish. "Go away."

"You said 'go away' three times," said Deena.

"Yes," said Trish. "Go away."

"But we have to shop for many things for your party."

"I am not going to have a party," said Trish. "I do not want to see anybody. I do not want anyone to see me."

Deena said, "Open the door. We need to talk this over."

At last, Trish opened the door. Trish had a big bag over her head. There were three holes in it. Two holes for her eyes. One hole for her nose.

"Why do you have a bag over your head?" said Deena.

"So you can't see me," said Trish.

"I know what you look like," said Deena.

"No, you don't," said Trish. "Just look at my hair!"

"Well, I agree, it's not your best cut," said Deena. "But many of us get cuts we don't like. We do not keep bags over our heads."

"All my pals will see me and laugh."

"They will not, Trish," said Deena.
"But they will make fun of
that silly bag."

"So what can we do?" said Trish.

"I know," said Deena. "We can look for a nice hat."

Trish had many hats. There were
green hats and yellow hats.
There were five hats with stripes
and five hats with stars.

Deena picked a green hat. "Let me
see how this one looks," she said.

Trish picked a hat with stars on it.
"Try this one," she said to Deena. So
Deena put on the hat. Then Trish put
a hat on top of the hat. Soon, Deena
had four hats on her head. Then
Trish had four hats on. Deena
laughed at Trish. Trish laughed at
Deena. Then they looked in the
mirror and laughed at themselves.

"I have a good idea. You can make it a funny hat party," said Deena.

"That is a good idea," said Trish. "I will do it!" So Trish asked all her pals to wear funny hats to her party. She couldn't wait to see them.

"This is the best party ever," said Deena.

"Yes, it is," said Trish.

All of Trish's pals ate cake and
sweet apples. All of them drank
milk. All of them sang songs and
played games. But no one said a
word about Trish's hair.